Workbook Answer Key

CB126688

1 ID

Grammar

1

b your, My
c his, His
d her, Her

2

a this
b these

3

b They're
c It's
d They're
e They're
f It's

4

b What are these? They're keys.
c What's this? It's a cell phone.
d What are these? They're books.
e What are these? They're pens.
f What's this? It's a computer.

Vocabulary

1

b cell phone
c key
d camera
e book
f computer
g bag
h pen

2

1 one
2 two
3 three
4 four
5 five
6 six
7 seven
8 eight
9 nine
10 ten

3

b one camera
c three passports
d two computers
e nine pens
f five bags
g four cell phones
h eight books

Listening

1

b
a

2

a Marcus
b Smith
c Elise
d Brooker

3

b F
c F
d T
e F

Pronunciation

1

b books
c name
d cell phone
e passports
f cameras

2 International

Grammar

1

are	're
is	'is
are	're
are	're

2

b 's
c 'm
d 're
e 're
f 's

3

c is
d are
e Is
f Are

4

b she is
c I am
d I'm not
e they aren't
f Personal answer

5

b How much is a hamburguer in New York City?
c How much is a movie ticket in Hong Kong?
d How much are donuts in Buenos Aires?
e How much is a cell phone in Madrid?
f How much are pens in Paris?

6

Personal answers.

Vocabulary

1

b Mexico
c Japan
d Germany
e Chile
f Spain

2

b She's American.
c She's Brazilian.
d He's Spanish.
e He's Japanese.
f He's German.
g She's Mexican.

3

b eighteen
c twenty-six
d twenty
e seventy
f sixty
g thirty-two
h one hundred

4

b eleven
c thirty-six
d forty-nine
e seventy-eight
f eighty-nine

5

2 thanks
3 How
4 is
5 are

Writing

1

b He's from Brazil.
c Is she Mexican?
d Where are they from?
e The cameras are from Japan.

2

a question mark
b period

3

b Where are you from?
c Are you from Australia?
d I'm from Chile.
e My name's Reiko.
f No, I'm from Germany.

4

1 My name's Reiko.
2 Where are you from? I'm from Chile.
3 Are you from Australia? No, I'm from Germany.

5

Personal answers.

Pronunciation

1

b 4
c 5
d 3
e 2
f 3
g 2
h 4
i 3
j 4

2

b American
c nationality
d Mexican
e movie
f seventy
g question
h Argentina
i eleven
j conversation

3 Family

Grammar

1

b How old is your sister?
c How old is your car?
d How old are your parents?
e How old are you?
f How old is your cell phone?
g How old are your children?
h How old is your computer?

2

Personal answers.

3

your
his
her
our
their

4

2 my
3 She
4 our
5 Their
6 We
7 It
8 They

5

b sisters'
c Tom's
d children's
e grandparents'

6

b has
c have
d have
e have
f has
g has

Pronunciation

2

country husband mother much son	camera family grandfather Japan thank that

Vocabulary

1

A	G	R	A	N	F	T	G	H	S	T	E	R	G
P	G	P	R	E	T	S	I	S	M	Q	D	A	R
G	R	A	N	D	M	O	T	H	E	R	A	U	A
H	A	P	H	H	U	S	B	A	N	D	U	G	N
S	N	S	O	N	B	D	H	T	R	H	G	H	D
A	D	M	O	G	R	W	I	F	E	T	H	T	D
Q	F	A	J	N	O	P	G	M	H	L	T	G	A
W	A	M	H	R	T	O	H	O	T	P	E	R	U
E	T	A	L	A	H	P	T	I	A	Y	R	A	G
I	H	N	O	N	E	S	U	N	F	V	S	T	H
N	E	S	U	D	R	F	R	E	G	H	J	H	T
P	R	T	S	M	O	T	H	E	R	E	M	E	E
G	R	A	F	A	T	H	E	R	I	F	E	R	R
D	F	T	D	Q	N	O	S	D	N	A	R	G	O

husband father son brother grandson	wife mother daughter sister granddaughter

2

b parents
c grandparents
d grandchildren

3

b 1
c 5
d 2
e 4

4

Personal answers.

Listening

1

4
3
1
2

2

b T
c T
d F
e F
f F

3

b Lara
c Anita
d Julia
e Fabio

4 Life

Grammar

1

- b speaks
- c eat
- d likes
- e live
- f have

2

- b He doesn't speak Spanish.
- c We don't eat meat.
- d She doesn't like soccer.
- e They don't live in Bogotá.
- f You don't have two sisters.

3

- b Does the movie start at 7 o'clock?
- c Do they finish work early?
- d Do Rob and Jodi live in New York?
- e Does she go home on the bus?
- f Do you speak English?

4

- b it does
- c they do
- d they don't
- e she doesn't
- f I do

5

- b It's two thirty.
- c It's ten fifteen. It's a quarter after ten.
- d It's three twenty-five. It's twenty-five after three.
- e It's eleven ten. It's ten after eleven.
- f It's twelve thirty-five. It's twenty five to one.

Pronunciation

1

- b eat, meet
- c for, your
- d name, same
- e night, white
- f not, what
- g one, son
- h two, you

Vocabulary

1

1. soccer player
2. artist
3. doctor
4. farmer
5. pilot
6. flight attendant
7. DJ
8. journalist
9. teacher

2

Tuesday
Wednesday
Thursday
Friday
Saturday
Sunday

3

- b gets up
- c finish
- d teach
- e get
- f has

4

Personal answers.

5

- a Good afternoon. Good evening.
- b Good night.

Writing

1

2. morning
3. breakfast
4. work
5. lunch
6. afternoon
7. finishes
8. evening
9. home
10. dinner
11. bed

2

Personal answers.

3

Personal answers.

5 Places

Grammar

1

2. There's
3. There are
4. there are
5. There's
6. There are
7. there's

2

- b some
- c a
- d some
- e some
- f a

3

- b Are there
- c Is there
- d Is there
- e Are there
- f Are there

4

- b there aren't
- c there is
- d there isn't
- e there are
- f there aren't

5

- b a
- c any
- d a
- e any
- f an

6

Personal answers.

Vocabulary

1

- b park
- c bridge
- d statue
- e museum
- f station
- g lake
- h river
- i square

2

- a the Empire State Building, the city, the movie theater, the park, a show, the zoo

b the city, the park, the street
c the street
d the Empire State Building

3

b pharmacy
c restroom
d subway

Pronunciation

1

conversation eight famous lake place they	inside night nine price time white

Listening

1

5
1
3, 4
6
2

2

b cheap
c old
d beautiful
e ugly
f expensive

3

b likes
c 30
d isn't
e is

6 Clothes

Grammar

1

b is wearing
c am playing
d are dancing
e are running
f are drinking

2

Personal answers.

3

usually
sometimes
not usually
never

4

b How often do you wear jeans?
c How often do you go to the movies?
d How often do you wear yellow?
e How often do you go to the gym?
f How often do you drink wine?

5

Personal answers.

Vocabulary

1

a blue
b brown
c green
d gray
e orange
f pink
g red
h yellow

2

Personal answers.

3

b boots
c hat
d jacket
e shirt
f jeans
g top
h skirt
i T-shirt
j pants
k shoes

4

lunch a cup of tea coffee a phone call	a computer game the piano the guitar soccer tennis
a book the paper an email	the housework the laundry

Pronunciation

2

homework old piano phone yellow	couch house noun outside tower

Writing

1

having
eating
walking

2

a, c, d

3

a Sydney.
b Prawns.
c They walk on the beach.

4

a @samsmith
b Personal answer.

5

Personal answers.

Notes

Notes

ISBN 9786685732269